My MOM is the BEST MOM

CLIFFORD HERRIOT

I'll tell every pug and poodle,

I'll tell every Irish setter,

My mom is the best mom.
There's simply no one better.

When I'm stressed or worried,
she keeps me safe and snug.

And when I'm feeling
sad and low,
she gives a gentle hug.

She has love enough for everyone, but always tells me why

I'm an extra special, bright and shining star up in her sky.

Mom always keeps
my bowl filled
with healthy things
to eat,

But she knows the day is better when we share a special treat.

when I'm scared to try new things

She's there to urge me on.

And she's happy to relax with me

on a warm and sunny lawn.

And helps me to chill out if I get too excited.

Listen up,
chihuahuas,
beagles,
huskies,
and
retrievers!

My mom is the best mom, and I'll make you all believers.

My mom and I share everything.

I even help her work.

And she's always very patient... even when I'm being a jerk.

Whether playing in the park,

Or reading books at home,

She finds new things
to share with me
no matter where
we roam.

Whether hiking
in the
mountains,

Or on a
city street,

Traveling together makes the journey twice as sweet.

She takes me to the seashore

For a day of sand and sun

Because she knows
how much I love
to chase the waves
and run.

Winter, summer, spring, or fall,

In any kind of weather,

As long as
we're together.

That my mom is the best for me and yours the best for you.

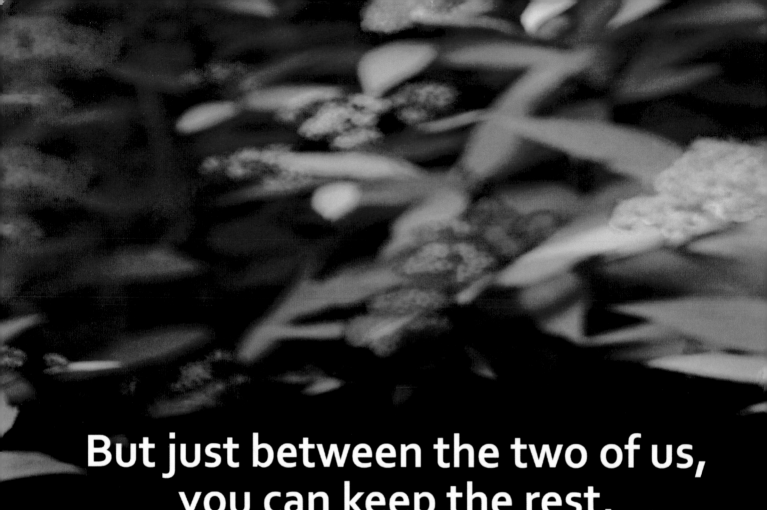

But just between the two of us,
you can keep the rest.
Of all the moms in all the world...

Mine is still
THE BEST!

ABOUT THE AUTHOR

...s based on dozens of interviews with dogs who ...ably convinced that their mom is the best mom ...e author, Clifford Herriot, is not the Dog Whisper- ...t dogs do whisper to him.

PHOTO CREDITS

Blas, Bodnar Photo, Bondarillia, CynoClub, DM Vector, DNF Style, DragonImages, Erika8213, Fotorince, Fotyma, GPoint Studio, Hay Dimitri, Irina Kashaeva, Leungchopan, LifeOnWhite, Racool Studio, RossHelen, SeventyFour Images, Sonyachny, Svetography, ThamKC, Twenty20Photos, Ulza, Wavebreak Media, YouraPechkin.

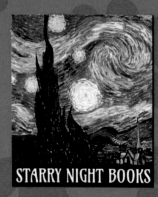

STARRY NIGHT BOOKS

Published by Starry Night Books